DEBORAH STEINBERG
psychotherapist for over 20 years, and has specialised in weight and food issues since the 1970s.

During 1985 to 1995, she was staff psychotherapist at the Institute for Rational Emotive Therapy in New York where she ran most of the weight control groups.

She is the author of *Stella Remembers* (a personal account of Ms Steinberg's family history based on the memoirs of her grandmother, Stella K. Abraham).

Ms Steinberg obtained her Masters degree in Social Work (MSW) from Columbia University in 1973 and is currently in private practice. She is married with a young son, Daniel, and lives in Florida.

WINDY DRYDEN was born in London in 1950. He has worked in psychotherapy and counselling for over twenty years, and is the author or editor of over ninety books, including *The Incredible Sulk* (Sheldon Press, 1992) and *Ten Steps to Positive Living* (Sheldon Press, 1994). Dr Dryden is Professor of Counselling at Goldsmiths College, University of London.

Overcoming Common Problems Series

For a full list of titles please contact
Sheldon Press, Marylebone Road, London NW1 4DU

The Assertiveness Workbook
A plan for busy women
JOANNA CUTMANN

Beating the Comfort Trap
DR WINDY DRYDEN AND JACK
GORDON

Birth Over Thirty Five
SHEILA KITZINGER

Body Language
How to read others' thoughts by their
gestures
ALLAN PEASE

Body Language in Relationships
DAVID COHEN

Calm Down
How to cope with frustration and anger
DR PAUL HAUCK

Cancer – A Family Affair
NEVILLE SHONE

Comfort for Depression
JANET HORWOOD

Coping Successfully with Hayfever
DR ROBERT YOUNGSON

Coping Successfully with Migraine
SUE DYSON

Coping Successfully with Pain
NEVILLE SHONE

Coping Successfully with PMS
KAREN EVENNETT

Coping Successfully with Panic Attacks
SHIRLEY TRICKETT

**Coping Successfully with Prostrate
Problems**
ROSY REYNOLDS

**Coping Successfully with Your
Hyperactive Child**
DR PAUL CARSON

**Coping Successfully with Your Irritable
Bowel**
ROSEMARY NICOL

**Coping Successfully with Your Second
Child**
FIONA MARSHALL

Coping with Anxiety and Depression
SHIRLEY TRICKETT

Coping with Blushing
DR ROBERT EDELMANN

Coping with Bronchitis and Emphysema
DR TOM SMITH

Coping with Candida
SHIRLEY TRICKETT

Coping with Chronic Fatigue
TRUDIE CHALDER

Coping with Cot Death
SARAH MURPHY

Coping with Crushes
ANITA NAIK

Coping with Cystitis
CAROLINE CLAYTON

Coping with Depression and Elation
DR PATRICK McKEON

Coping with Postnatal Depression
FIONA MARSHALL

Coping with Psoriasis
PROFESSOR RONALD MARKS

Coping with Schizophrenia
DR STEVEN JONES AND DR FRANK
TALLIS

Coping with Strokes
DR TOM SMITH

Coping with Suicide
DR DONALD SCOTT

Coping with Thyroid Problems
DR JOAN GOMEZ

Coping with Thrush
CAROLINE CLAYTON

Curing Arthritis Exercise Book
MARGARET HILLS AND JANET
HORWOOD

Overcoming Common Problems Series

Overcoming Common Problems Series

Overcoming Common Problems

HOW TO STICK
TO A DIET

Deborah Steinberg MSW
and Dr Windy Dryden

sheldon **PRESS**

First published in Great Britain in 1996 by
Sheldon Press, SPCK, Marylebone Road, London NW1 4DU

British Library Cataloguing-in-Publication Data
A catalogue record for this book is available from the British Library

ISBN 0–85969–739–8

Photoset by Deltatype Ltd, Ellesmere Port, Cheshire
Printed in Great Britain by Arrowsmiths Ltd, Bristol

Contents

Introduction

This is not a book that advocates a particular diet. We are not trying to sell you the Steinberg-Dryden diet plan. Nor are we necessarily recommending that you lose weight. If, however, you have decided to lose weight or have been advised to go on a particular diet (say, to reduce your blood cholesterol level if it is high), then this book will outline a number of ways that will help you to implement the programme you have selected. In particular, we will help you to identify and change self-defeating thinking that leads you to give in to the many temptations that you will face along the way. We will discuss a number of ways in which you can change your behaviour so that you can gain control of your eating. We will also discuss how you can use mental imagery, exercise and assertion to help you achieve your goals. In short, if you follow our advice, this book will help you to stick to your diet. Whatever the reason for you following a diet, what we have to say will help.

Why go on a diet? Why lose weight? The answers to these questions are much more complex than was once thought. You may be eating the wrong foods or wrong combinations of foods or be sufficiently overweight for this to be putting your health at risk. If this is the case, then it is important that you consult your doctor in the first instance. Your doctor may well suggest that you see a dietician or a nutritionist who will suggest a sensible diet or weight loss programme that will help you to develop healthy eating habits. Take this advice. Don't try to develop a diet or lose weight on your own, and please think twice before you go on any faddy diets – they may be number one in the bestseller list today, but be on the growing scrap-heap of such books tomorrow. Also, we urge you not to go on any kind of unsupervised crash diet, as this will probably do you more harm than good in the long term.

You may also want to diet for aesthetic reasons (you think you will look better) or for fitness reasons (you think you will feel better physically). Both these reasons are fine as long as your weight goal is a healthy one. We say this because a number of people wish to achieve a weight that is too low for their body shape, so it is worth checking your plan with your doctor or a dietician before you start.

Many diets have been criticized for teaching people only how to lose weight. A popular saying sums it up . . . 'Losing weight is easy, I've done it hundreds of times.' The key to any successful diet for weight loss is weight maintenance.

Perhaps you should stop for a moment and think about your reasons for wanting to lose weight. You may wish to go on a diet because you think that being thinner will raise your self-esteem. In our opinion, this motive is an unhealthy one. It reflects an attitude that, in effect, says that your worth is dependent on your weight. If you think about it, this is nonsense. While being thinner may be advantageous in itself, it can never prove that you are a worthier person unless you define yourself as such. If you think in this way, you will soon find that even if you lose weight you will still suffer from low self-esteem. If this happens, you may well attempt to lose *more* weight and sow the seeds of an eating disorder. Alternatively, you may see that food does *not* solve your problems and so turn to food for comfort, putting *on* weight and feeling less worthy as a result. If you suffer from low self-esteem you will benefit more from counselling than dieting. See a reputable helping professional or ask your doctor to suggest someone. Food will not solve self-esteem and other emotional problems; its purpose is to keep us alive and give us energy.

Sound nutrition, exercise, and a rational state of mind are essential for long-term weight loss results.

The state of your mind is emphasized in this book by teaching useful thinking habits and positive behavioural

2

changes related to food. Also included are methods to overcome emotional eating using rational thinking, imagery techniques and assertive training skills.

Equally important is a low-fat diet and adequate exercise. Experts even suggest that a sensible exercise programme can help stimulate clear, rational thinking.

You may be one of the growing number of people who are constantly dieting (between the times when you are overeating, that is). Research shows that 'yo-yo' dieting, as this phenomenon is called, is bad for your health in that it damages the skeleton. This is because when you lose weight, you also lose bone density, which isn't replaced when you regain weight. The result may be an increased risk of osteoporosis (brittle bone disease). If you are a 'yo-yo' dieter, please do see your doctor, who may investigate the reasons behind this. For example, you may be trying to lose too *much* weight, with the result that you put on weight once you have stopped dieting. Alternatively, you may give up on your weight-loss programme as soon as the going gets tough, only to return to it in the vain hope that this time it will work. Or your constant dieting may mask a psychological problem that you are trying unsuccessfully to solve by attempting to lose weight. Your doctor will point you in the right direction so that you can begin to discover the reasons for your 'yo-yo' behaviour.

Your desire to lose weight may also be due to an eating disorder. If you constantly 'feel fat' when others are telling you how thin and gaunt you look, if you are scared of putting on even the tiniest amount while, at the same time, you are always thinking of food, or if you compulsively exercise to lose weight when, again, people are showing concern that you are 'too thin', then these may well be signs that you have anorexia nervosa. If this applies to you, you need skilled professional help, although of course you are likely to be the last person to realize this. Please do see your doctor, though, if you see yourself in our description. Also, if you swing between bingeing and purging your food (for example, vomiting and/or using laxatives to get rid of the food that you have binged on), you may well be bulimic and, if so, again, you need professional help.

As you can see, deciding to go on a diet is not a simple business. While we cannot deal with your particular reason for wanting to follow a diet or lose weight, we do urge you to think long and hard about it before making the commitment. Consulting helpful professionals along the way is especially valuable. Once you and others are sure that following a particular diet or losing weight is in the best interests of your health, this is where we come in. Maybe you have just been told that you have diabetes or that you need cut out fatty and other foods that are high in cholesterol. If so, you will have been given dietary advice, but not necessarily have the skills to comply with your new dietary programme. In this book we will suggest ways to help you stick to your diet and maintain a healthy you.

This book is based on an approach to counselling known as rational emotive behaviour therapy (REBT), invented by Albert Ellis and developed by, among others, Maxie C. Maultsby Jr and Paul Hauck. We have drawn on their ideas in this book and wish to acknowledge their healthy influence on our thinking. As this book only explores the relevance of REBT to sticking to a diet, we recommend that the interested reader consult the works of Paul Hauck and Windy Dryden, whose self-help books on a wide variety of personal development issues are also published by Sheldon Press.

1

Think Positive –
Finding Your 'Self-talk'

The way we think largely determines how we feel and how we react. What we say to ourselves, our 'self-talk', affects our emotions and our behaviour.

What do you mean by 'self-talk'?
These are automatic thoughts – the statements we make to ourselves, sometimes without even realizing it. Our minds are constantly churning out thoughts and these direct our actions and reactions to events.

How do I know what statements I'm making? I'm not aware of my self-talk
The first step is to realize you have such automatic thoughts – we all do! Then, the trick is to recognize the harmful, self-defeating thoughts and to replace them with logical, positive statements that will help you.

What does this have to do with my eating habits?
Quite a bit. Let's explore further.

Self-defeating self-talk in four situations

Let's examine some typical situations in which self-defeating thinking will block effective use of a diet.

Situation 1: the party
You're at a party. The food looks great and everyone else

appears to be enjoying it without having to pick and choose.

Self-defeating thoughts

1 'I can't stand being deprived.'

2 'I want that food. I must have it now.'

3 'I can't stand being the only one who has to watch their diet. I hate being different.'

Situation 2: the stressful visit

You've been doing well with your diet but you feel stressed. Your in-laws are visiting and you've already started cheating on the diet. You're not feeling so well and you are upset.

Self-defeating thoughts

1 'I'm so nervous that I need more food to tolerate the anxiety.'

2 'What's the point of stopping? The damage is already done.'

3 'I'm a failure. This proves I can't ever do it.'

Situation 3: the 'plateau'

You've been sticking to your diet, but have reached a 'plateau' where, for a while, you seem to be making no progress. You're feeling frustrated and impatient.

Self-defeating thoughts

1 'Sticking to a diet should be easier, not such a continuous struggle and effort.'

2 'It's impossible – I'll never succeed.'

3 'I can't stand this frustration any longer!'

Situation 4: the comparison

You and your best friend are both on a diet, but she's doing better and coping more easily. You're feeling angry and somewhat resentful.

Self-defeating thoughts

1 'It's not fair that I have to work harder than others to stick to my diet.'

2 'It's awful that life is so unfair to me.'

3 'There must be a magical, easy way to control my eating, so I'll wait for it.'

In each case, such self-defeating thoughts make it more difficult to handle the situation. In fact, such thinking will, most likely, cause you to eat the wrong foods, be angry with yourself and feel hopeless. And *that* could lead you to stray from your diet even more!

But, remember, you don't need to be a slave to your self-defeating automatic thoughts. You can make your self-talk work *for* you rather than *against* you! The first step is to learn to identify the problem thoughts.

Finding your negative self-talk

Look again at our examples of self-defeating self-talk. We call such thinking irrational because it is not logical or realistic and it leads you to act against your own best interests.

You can probably find plenty of examples of these kinds of thoughts every day. A good exercise is to look for and eliminate self-talk that contains thoughts like these:

Demands or absolute commands

These are phrases like 'I must', 'I need', and 'I have to'. This kind of thinking is irrational because it assumes that you have the absolute power to make all your commands come true – that you run the universe!

Putting yourself down

These are thoughts like 'I'm no good, I'm bad, I'm worthless'. They are irrational because you are usually condemning *everything* about yourself because of just one or two things you did 'wrong'. In other words, you are rating your whole self instead of just rating some 'bad' traits or some 'bad' behaviour.

'Awfulizing'

This is the kind of thinking that turns normal problems into catastrophes. When you do this, you are exaggerating the 'badness' of a situation, thereby making it much worse.

Low frustration tolerance

This kind of thinking makes you unwilling to tolerate discomfort. It is characterized by statements like 'I can't stand it', 'This is too difficult' and so on. It is irrational because it fails to recognize that we all need to put up with some of the hassles and inconvenience of daily living.

Turning your self-defeats into victories

Let's now look back at our four difficult situations and see what kinds of new, rational self-statements we can substitute for the negative ones to help us handle tough spots more appropriately.

Situation 1: the party

Self-defeating thoughts	Positive alternatives
1 'I can't stand being deprived.'	'I don't *like* being deprived, but I *can* stand it.'

2 'I want that food. I must have it now.'

'I don't *need* everything I simply *want*. While I may want that *food*, I don't want all the problems that go with eating food that is bad for my health. It's hard to pass up lovely food, but I'll feel much better very soon if I do.'

3 'I can't stand being the only one who has to watch their diet. I hate being different.'

'I don't like being different and limited in my food choices, but it's not that terrible! If I remember my diet goals, it will help. No pain, no gain.'

Situation 2: the stressful visit

Self-defeating thoughts

Positive alternatives

1 'I'm so nervous that I need more food to tolerate the anxiety.'

'Eating just what I feel like won't eliminate my anxiety. It may distract me momentarily, but it will really just give me an additional problem to handle. I certainly can tolerate some anxiety and can find a better way to reduce it.'

2 'What's the point of stopping? The damage is already done.'

'If I don't stop now, I'll certainly make the problem worse. Losing one battle doesn't lose the war! I can definitely get back on track, remember my goals and refocus.'

9

3 'I'm a failure. This proves I can't ever do it.'

'I may have failed to stick to my diet, but that hardly proves that I am a failure as a person. I've certainly succeeded at many things in my life! Even my past 'failures' don't prevent me from succeeding at this in the future.'

Situation 3: the 'plateau'

Self-defeating thoughts

Positive alternatives

1 'Sticking to a diet should be easier, not such a continuous struggle and effort.'

'Why should something that is hard be easier just because I command it? Sticking to a diet *can* be difficult, but I'd better remember, "No pain, no gain".'

2 'It's impossible – I'll never succeed!'

'Sticking to a diet may be difficult at times, but "difficult" hardly means "impossible".'

3 'I can't stand this frustration any longer!'

'I *can* stand a little frustration, even though it is unpleasant. It is part of life and I can still enjoy myself in many ways.'

Situation 4: the comparison

Self-defeating thoughts

Positive alternatives

1 'It's not fair that I have to work harder than others to stick to my diet.'

'Where did I get the idea that all things in life would be fair or equally easy? Some things will be easier for me than for others – other things more difficult. But that's no reason for me to stop trying to be the best I can!'

2 'It's awful that life is so unfair to me.'

'It's unfortunate that this is difficult, but it's hardly a disaster or the worst thing that could happen. I'm making it *more* difficult by "awfulizing".'

3 'There must be a magical, easy way to control my eating, so I'll wait for it.'

'Looking for a magical solution won't work, but sticking with a solid plan will. There's no short cut. I'd better accept reality and make the effort.'

You're probably beginning to see that one of the most important aspects of your diet is your attitude – how you're thinking about yourself, about your diet and sticking to it.

Your determination and persistence in identifying and challenging irrational thinking are crucial. They can help you succeed in making the positive changes that will allow you to control your eating permanently.

2

Think Positive –
Changing Your 'Self-talk'

The way we think and talk to ourselves will strongly influence how we deal with food.

The last chapter explained that we're often not aware of our self-talk. How can I know if my self-statements are in need of change?

Notice your emotional and behavioural reactions to situations. If you are feeling depressed, anxious, hostile, guilty, overly-frustrated or if you are reacting in a self-defeating way – overeating, eating when not hungry or eating the wrong (high-fat) kinds of foods too frequently – the chances are that your thinking is negative and self-defeating. See if you can catch what you're saying to yourself and recognize that you can correct and change it to a more rational, more positive self-dialogue.

How can I practise this?

Good question! Take a look at the typical self-defeating statements that follow. Use this opportunity to develop *new*, more effective self-talk.

Fifteen negative self-statements to correct

Circle those self-defeating ideas that apply to you and write your own, new, rational statements in the blank space provided beside each statement.

12

Negative self-statements	*Your positive alternatives*
1 'As I haven't succeeded yet, that proves I can't do it.'	_____ _____ _____ _____ _____
2 'Self-control is too hard. It shouldn't be this hard.'	_____ _____ _____ _____ _____
3 'It would be easier to control my eating tomorrow.'	_____ _____ _____ _____ _____
4 'Other people get away with overeating, or eating unhealthily, and so should I. It's not fair.'	_____ _____ _____ _____

5 'I don't feel like stopping. I shouldn't have to
do what I don't feel like
doing.'

6 'I can't stand being deprived.'

7 'It's my nature to eat
whatever's around. I was
born this way and I can't
help it.'

8 'I need immediate com-
fort, especially when I've
had a bad day.'

9 'I'm too old and too set in
   my habits to change. It's
   hopeless.'

   _____
   _____
   _____
   _____
   _____

10 'Why should I change? I
   could be dead next
   week.'

   _____
   _____
   _____
   _____

11 'It's not just difficult to
   change my eating habits,
   it's *awful*!'

   _____
   _____
   _____
   _____

12 'I can't resist the temptations. I have no willpower.'

   _____
   _____
   _____
   _____

13 'I need the food to make
me feel better and to
reduce stress.'

_____

_____

_____

_____

_____

14 'Eating is easier than facing my problems.'

_____

_____

_____

_____

_____

15 'I'm not motivated and I
need to be motivated to
follow a particular diet.'

_____

_____

_____

_____

_____

*Did we miss any irrational
thoughts you have? If so,
list them here.*

*What new beliefs can you
generate to replace your old
irrational thoughts?*

_____   _____

_____   _____

_____   _____

If you've had to follow a special diet or been overweight and losing weight has been a struggle, the chances are that at least several of the statements listed above are very familiar to you. Consciously or unconsciously you've been believing and repeating these self-defeating ideas to yourself for a long time. It's time to give them up. Holding on to any of them will sabotage your best efforts. The first step is to identify which statements you recognize as your own strongly held beliefs.

Become aware of how strongly your automatic thoughts and beliefs have dominated your relationships with food and know that you *can* change them! For now, begin to become aware of your own self-talk. As a first step, keep this list with you and look for your own silent, or not so silent, self-talk. When you find it, correct it. You've now had some solid practice in doing exactly that!

3

Change Your Behaviour
and Put Yourself in Control

In Chapter 1, we discussed some of the ways you think about yourself – and about your diet and sticking to it. In this chapter, we'll examine some useful changes you can make in the ways you act and *re*act to food. These behavioural suggestions are designed to help you achieve your goal of permanent control.

Remember, the food habits you've developed may be well practised from years of use, but that doesn't mean you can't learn to make changes and develop new routines that will give you permanent control over your eating habits and success in keeping to your diet. You *can* learn a new way of relating to food – if you truly want to and are willing to put in effort and practise. Below is a list of 20 behavioural changes you can begin to make today.

I do want to change, and I'm willing to work at it, but making so many changes sounds like an impossibly tall order.

Give yourself time to integrate these new habits. A practical approach might be to try one new suggestion each week rather than try to make *all* of the changes at once. That would be unrealistic and probably frustrating for you. Go slowly and develop a pace that works for you – but stay with it.

I've had bad eating habits most of my life. Is it realistic to think I can change them for good?

Yes! Changes that seem awkward at first will become more comfortable as you practise them. The key is to stick with them. Think about any other new activities you have begun – like learning a foreign language or playing tennis for the first time. Initial difficulty fades with practice and persistence. Keep going, and ask for help when you feel it would be useful.

With each suggested behavioural change we list below, we will explain the reasoning behind the recommendation. It is important that the changes you're making make sense to you.

Twenty behavioural changes you can make now

Whenever you eat, make eating your only activity

Many of us who have difficulty with our diet or weight control are not aware of how much we are actually eating. Talking on the phone, watching television, working and so on, are all distracting and keep us from paying attention to what we are eating. Whenever you eat, give your full attention to your meal and notice what and how much food you consume.

Restrict your eating to a single, designated room

This limits your association with food to a specific place. And it keeps other rooms in the house 'safe' by declaring them off-limits for food.

Sit down while you eat – and always sit in the same place

If you typically eat while you stand, walk or move about, you may not be conscious of what and how much you are eating. Sitting down focuses your attention more directly on the activity of eating. By eating in the same place, you identify and associate that spot with the idea that it is the only area in which you should eat.

Store food only in the kitchen

This restricts the most powerful triggers to eating to a single area. The temptation to reach for food will be much less than if food is stored throughout the house.

Avoid buying or bringing home any non-nutritional foods

These 'empty' foods can actually make you hungrier! Don't make things harder on yourself. Decide now that these unnecessary temptations are out of bounds.

Shop for groceries only after eating

You will then be less likely to buy foods impulsively – especially foods you don't need.

When you buy food, stick to your shopping list

This helps you guard against impulse shopping and shopping in response to advertisements. Make sure your list is complete. Then, once you're in the shop, refuse to buy any extra items.

Leave at least one bite of food on your plate at the end of a meal

By doing this, you show yourself *you're* in control – that food doesn't control you. Ths is a good exercise for all members of the 'clean plate club'.

Join someone who is eating and have only a tea, coffee or cold drink

Assuming you've eaten already and are joining someone who hasn't, this is a good opportunity for you to refuse to overeat just because food is available. Develop your 'won't' power.

Decide in advance to take home a doggy-bag from a restaurant

Learn to stop eating when you're satisfied and to save the remainder for another meal. You don't *have* to finish it because it is on your plate.

Stop eating before you feel really full

This will help you become aware of feeling satisfied during a meal – as opposed to the feeling of being overfull, with all the negative consequences of discomfort and overeating.

Take a three-minute break or a bathroom break during the meal

This helps you learn to take your time and eat more slowly. You don't need to finish the meal in 30 seconds! This is a particularly good exercise for hurried eaters.

Buy an ice-cream, enjoy a few bites then throw the rest away

Use any sweet treat to practise this exercise. Show yourself that you can enjoy a taste without having to devour the whole thing.

Delay the urge to eat – set a timer for 20 minutes

The urge will pass whether you give in to it or ignore it. See what happens by delaying the urge with a timer. People frequently report that they get absorbed in some other activity and forget the urge to eat, which, shortly before, had seemed important.

Delay eating until your body 'asks' for food

Constantly eating eliminates our ability to experience hunger sensations, which, frequently, are the best indication of when it's 'time to eat'.

Get rid of, store or lend out all the clothes in your wardrobe that do not fit now

Why put your life on hold until you achieve your ideal weight? Start living again *now*. Don't torture yourself by remembering when those clothes fitted and demanding that you be able to wear them again now.

Buy new clothes for the size you are right now

It's important to accept yourself as you are now while you're working towards your goal. This helps develop self-acceptance and will actually help you move more easily towards reaching your goals.

Eat in front of others, especially if you are a 'closet eater'.

It's important to give yourself permission to eat – no matter what your diet or how much you weigh.

Slow down! *Put utensils down between bites, chew each mouthful at least 20 times, take at least 20 minutes to finish a meal*

These steps help you not to overeat and to walk away from a meal feeling satisfied. Research shows that it takes at least 20 minutes for your brain to get a message of the satisfaction of hunger. Therefore, slowing down can help you to leave the table feeling satisfied (but not overly full) and to taste your food more fully.

Throw away the scale – or weigh yourself once a week at most

This is to avoid you making the scales dictate your mood each day. For example, if the scales give you a 'good report', you have a good day; a 'bad report' signals a bad day, and so on.

It is best to limit your weighing of yourself to once a week because of your body's natural fluctuations in fluid balance. These changes produce temporary gains and losses in your weight, which could falsely encourage or discourage you. Try, instead, to measure the changes in your figure every few weeks. You'll have a pretty good idea of your progress anyway by how your clothes fit!

My personal 'change list'

Everyone has special weaknesses or problem areas of their own. In the spaces below, add your own suggestions for changes you would like to make in your own life and say why they would help.

1 _____

_____

_____

_____

2 _____

_____

_____

_____

3 _____

_____

_____

_____

4

Using Mental Imagery:
Picture Yourself in Control

Thinking positive and changing your behaviour are key ingredients in your efforts to achieve permanent control over your eating habits. Imagery, or the process of visualizing, is another important technique you can use in your pursuit of a healthier you. In this chapter, we'll describe this valuable technique in detail.

How will using something like imagery help me stick to my diet?

There are several ways you can use imagery. For example, with visualizing techniques you can rehearse a forthcoming event that you expect will give you trouble or you can replay a past event you didn't manage as well as you would have liked. Experiment with these techniques and you'll see what powerful aids they can be to controlling your eating.

Can you give me a concrete example of how I might use imagery to help me stick to my diet?

Yes! Let's imagine that next week you're attending an important business function that will have a buffet at midday. Buffets have always been difficult for you and you're beginning to feel anxious even thinking about this forthcoming event. Read on, for step-by-step instructions.

Rational-emotive imagery: here's how it works

1: Picture the scene

Find a comfortable place where you can sit uninterrupted for two to three minutes (that's all it takes!). Close your eyes and picture yourself at the buffet. See yourself in that scene, see the dazzling array of food, see everyone eating. Most important, let yourself experience the feelings you have while you're at the buffet. Allow yourself to feel the anxiety, the worry, the pressure to eat indiscriminately, the constant fear of losing control and 'blowing it'.

2: Change what you feel

Now it's time to change those negative, self-defeating feelings into feelings you can handle, and you are elected for the job! You created the anxiety and nervousness and you *can* change them into more appropriate feelings – such as mild discomfort, concern or even frustration. These are feelings you can deal with effectively.

3: Change your feelings by changing what you say to yourself

You change the feeling by changing what you are saying to yourself. Let's look first at what you might be saying to make yourself feel bad – that is, anxious and nervous – and then we'll look at the positive things you could be saying to yourself instead.

Anxiety – provoking inner dialogue

'I must not give in to these temptations, but it's too difficult, it's impossible. I can't resist. This is too hard. I'm going to fail, give in to temptation and feel awful.'

As a result of this kind of 'self-talk', you feel discouraged, overwhelmed and out of control. If you believe what you've just told yourself, you may be unable to resist indulging at the buffet.

More rational inner dialogue (which leads to a healthier reaction)

'This is difficult but I *can* handle it. I can have something sensible before I arrive. I'll feel satisfied and less likely to stuff myself. These buffets are tempting, but they're not impossible to manage. I can see what's served, figure out what's on my diet plan, walk away for a few minutes by myself and determine to stick to what I should eat. I can remind myself that momentary discomfort and long-term gains are definitely better than immediate satisfaction and long-term pain.'

You're probably beginning to see how such a rational dialogue can help you reduce your anxiety and react more constructively to a difficult situation.

A reminder

The way to change your self-defeating feelings, such as nagging anxiety, is to change your inner dialogue. You can do this in a matter of minutes, but, don't forget, this new skill takes practice. In order to strengthen and 'internalize' your rational self-talk skills, you will need to practise them daily for at least 30 days.

A review of rational-emotive imagery

Think of a situation you are dreading or one that you handled poorly and may be berating yourself about. Find a comfortable position and close your eyes. Feel those uncomfortable feelings. Then, still picturing the same exact situation, change your self-defeating feelings by changing what you are saying to yourself.

Reinforcement and penalties

To ensure that you practise this imagery exercise at least once a day for the next 30 days, think about the following.

How can I use reinforcement as an incentive to practise my imagery?

Positive reinforcement works by giving you a positive reward when you do some kind of work. Think of something that you like to do practically every day, like calling a certain friend or having your morning coffee. Will you agree for the next 30 days to call your friend or have your coffee only *after* you've practised your rational emotive imagery? (This way, your practising will be reinforced by a pleasant experience.) Give it a try! But remember, on any day that you *don't* practise, no coffee and no call to your friend! Agreed?

How do penalties work?

Penalties work in the reverse way to reinforcement, by giving you an unpleasant experience if you neglect part of your plan. Think of something that you dislike doing, like cleaning or calling your in-laws. On any day that you forget or choose *not* to practise your rational emotive imagery, you then agree to stay up one extra hour cleaning or calling your in-laws. But, if you *do* practise the imagery, you can go to bed at your usual time.

What reinforcement and penalties achieve

The purpose of reinforcement and penalties is to give you powerful, 'custom-designed' incentives to follow through with the imagery practice. If you follow this imagery exercise diligently for 30 days, you will most likely be pleased with the new control you'll have acquired over formerly difficult situations.

More ways to use your imagery skills

Use a role model

Is there someone you know who has succeeded in sticking to their diet? Picture this person in your situation. How might they handle the tough situation you face? What might they think? Get a clear picture of how they would handle themselves and what kinds of things they would be saying to themselves. Better yet, talk to them and ask them how they have handled such situations and would manage if faced with your challenge. In your mind's eye, picture yourself acting and feeling in ways that would ensure the outcome you truly desire. Then, start putting your imagery into action!

Make it unappealing

A technique that is powerful (but does not help everyone) is to picture the worst, with foods that you're struggling to give up. For example, one woman had difficulty resisting a certain chocolate dessert. She cured herself fast by picturing it spoiled and covered with mould whenever she felt the urge to have some. Another learned to 'see' foods not on her diet as 'poison' and so was able to resist being tempted by them. You can try these unusual approaches – or create some of your own that meet your individual needs.

Picture the amount of weight you'll lose (or gain!)

Another successfully used visualization technique is the following. Take a 0.5 kg (1 lb) of fat and place it in a plastic bag. You will most likely find the sight unappealing (to say the least!). Whenever you find yourself forgetting your weight goals and tempted to stray, take out that bag of fat from the fridge or freezer or simply picture the fat in the bag. Remembering the image of the fat can be a strong reminder to you of your weight loss goals.

Remember . . .

Practice and repetition are the keys to using imagery effectively. Your responses to food are largely learned habits. You can learn new ways of responding to food – ways that are more compatible with your long-term goals.

5

Conquer Your 'Emotional Eating'

Overcoming emotional eating may be the most important step you can take in developing permanent control over your diet. This means eliminating eating done out of frustration, rage, anxiety, boredom, depression, guilt and so on. It also means relearning to eat on the basis of *hunger*, energy requirements and physiological needs.

I tend to eat off and on all day. I don't even know when I'm really hungry. How do I begin to take control of my eating?

First, you must closely observe your present eating behaviour – including what you eat, when you eat most, how much you eat and so on. To help you do this, the food diary chart on page 34 is a most valuable tool. It is meant to be used to gather important information that only you can provide. The idea behind it is that until you observe what you do with food, you have little chance of solving the problem effectively. No one's eating patterns are exactly like anyone else's, so keeping a daily record will give you information about exactly what, and under what circumstances, *you* are eating.

I don't like paperwork. Is keeping records really necessary?

Actually, keeping a food diary is quite simple – and it gets easier as you do it. It should take no more than 5 to 15 minutes a day to do. Keeping written logs like these is a proven method of taking and keeping control of problem behaviour – from overeating to smoking and gambling. Try it for at least one week and give yourself a chance to learn some valuable (and surprising!) information about your eating patterns.

1 Date	2 Time/ strength of hunger (1–10)	3 Food/ liquid consumed	4 Alternative behaviour	5 Mood	6 Context	7 Self-statement
	5.45 p.m. (3)	(Thinking about going to fridge.)	Bath	Restless	Home	Instead of attacking the fridge, I can take a bath to unwind.
	6.45 p.m. (5)	Glass tomato juice Grilled salmon ½ baked potato Broccoli, Salad 1 teaspoon dressing Tea		OK	Kitchen	Now I can really enjoy my dinner!
	10.30 p.m. (1)	Ice-cream	Manicure	Lonely	Home	Ice-cream won't help my lonely feeling. I'll do something nice for myself instead.

Fighting the irresistible urge

From time to time, most of us have urges, temptations or cravings about certain foods. These cravings may be so strong they sometimes feel like addictions. Such cravings are likely to have a strong emotional component, which makes it seem impossible to resist them. But, by stopping for a few seconds before giving in to the urge, it's possible to intercept the feelings that make you feel so out of control. Here's how.

Answer these **before** *you give in*

Copy the questions in the box below onto an index or plain post card that you can carry with you. Whenever you feel an irresistible urge to break your diet, going through these questions with yourself can break the 'spell'.

---

1 What am I craving? (Name the food or foods.)

2 What was happening just before I began to feel this craving?

3 What result can I expect if I give in to this temptation? How will I feel?

4 Is giving in to the urge the best or the only way to handle it?

5 Would some alternative activity work to satisfy or distract me?

6 Which do I choose this time: immediate gratification or mild frustration in exchange for long-term success?

If I choose immediate gratification, I will do one alternative activity for at least 15 minutes first.

6

Talk Yourself *Into* –
Not Out of –
Sticking to Your Diet Plan

It goes without saying that you want to look and feel your best! And you know that sticking to your diet is the surest way to reach that goal.

So why do I sometimes resist – or find it hard to follow – even the simplest, most flexible diet?

One answer is that body weight, food and eating all have important and powerful meanings for you. These meanings may not be rational – that is, they may not make logical sense – but they can still determine how comfortable, and how successful you are with any diet.

For me, eating was – and often still is – a way of pleasing people. Is that an example of a meaning that doesn't make sense?

A perfect example! If you were praised as a child for 'eating it all up', you may overeat as an adult because you still expect that approval – especially when you are a dinner guest.

Obstacles you put in your way

Let's take a look at some of the other messages many people tell themselves about eating, overeating and being overweight. Simply recognizing the ones that apply to you is a key step towards breaking free from their hold on you.

In the following list of statements, tick those that get in the way of your efforts to stick to your diet.

Statements	*Challenge*
☐ Eating was the way I first learned to get comfort and pleasure.	Is eating the only *or* the best way *now* for me to get comfort and pleasure?
☐ I would lose my identity if I lost my weight. There is something scary about not knowing who I would be as a slimmer person.	Is staying overweight the only *or* the best way *now* for me to maintain my identity? Is it the only way to feel secure with myself?
☐ Staying overweight was how I rebelled and said no to my family, society and anyone who had ideas about how I should look.	Is staying overweight the only *or* the best way I have *now* to be assertive and to make my own decisions about how I want to look?
☐ Gaining weight was the way I learned to get attention and sympathy at home.	Is remaining overweight the only *or* the best way I have *now* to get attention?
☐ Overeating and being overweight keep me safe from sexual attention. If I'm overweight, I am left alone.	Are these the only *or* the best ways to say no and to be left alone?
☐ Being overweight was a way to stay safe, to excuse myself for poor performance and to lower people's expectations of me.	Are being fat and staying 'safe' really the best ways for me to function *now*? Does risk-taking have to be frightening?

☐ Staying overweight was how I felt powerful and effective in my world.

Is staying overweight the only *or* the best way to be taken seriously and to make an impact?

☐ Staying overweight is easier than facing the other problems I would have as a slimmer person.

Is avoiding weight loss and good health the only *or* the best way to handle life's challenges?

☐ Eating gives me immediate gratification and pleasure. I don't have to wait.

Is immediate gratification the only *or* the best way to get pleasure and satisfaction? Is it worth the price in the long run?

☐ Food is the way to celebrate!

Are food and eating the only *or* the best ways to celebrate? Do I have to overindulge just because it's a celebration?

☐ Eating was how I stifled unacceptable feelings like anger.

Is eating the best *or* only way to deal with these feelings *now*?

☐ Eating keeps me connected with my childhood and my family, where food was always 'pushed'.

Is eating the only *or* the best way *now* for me to maintain family ties?

Overcoming these obstacles

Are some of the above statements familiar to you? Have you come to conclusions like these, as a way of coping with life's difficult situations? Do you repeat them to yourself to explain why you've failed to stick to your diet? If so, these self-defeating statements may be sabotaging your pursuit of health and/or weight loss and a happier life.

It's time to stop talking yourself out of your diet! Follow the next three steps and you'll see how.

1: Identify the self-defeating statements that apply to you most

If you haven't done so tick those statements above that get in the way of your plans.

2: Challenge those statements!

You've already begun to do this by reading the 'challenge' questions beneath each of the above statements. Read the questions again. Each time you catch yourself repeating one of your 'sabotage sentences', immediately ask – and answer – the challenge question beneath it.

3: Replace each self-defeating statement with an honest, self-strengthening one

There *are* better ways for you to handle tough situations today. Your eating patterns in the past, and even now, may be your attempt to take care of yourself under difficult conditions. The real questions are 'Is this the best or the only way I have *now* to do that?', 'Is this serving me well now?' and 'Did it ever?' Now is the time to re-educate yourself. Teach yourself new messages that get you what you want – a healthy body and self-control!

7

Eat Less Fat – It's More Fattening Than You think!

A calorie is a calorie is a calorie, right? Wrong! Research has shown that calories from fat are much more fattening than those from other kinds of foods. If you are trying to be healthier or lose weight, reducing your fat intake may be the most crucial change you make to your diet.

Do you mean I can eat as much as I want of other foods as long as I cut my fat intake right down?

No! To be healthy and lose weight, you must reduce the *total* number of calories you consume. But, as fat contains more calories than other foods – carbohydrates or protein, for example – the lower the proportion of *fat* calories within your total daily calorie allowance the better.

I've heard of something called a 'setpoint'. Does that mean I'm stuck at a certain weight?

Yes and no. Many researchers believe there is an individual 'setpoint' for body fat – that is, a 'built-in' level of fat that's natural and healthy for you. It's not wise to try to reduce your weight to much below your setpoint. However, a low-fat diet and regular exercise may help you gradually lower your setpoint over time.

Why *are fat calories the most fattening?*

Fat is the worst enemy of the overweight person because each gram of fat contains more than twice as many calories as a gram of carbohydrates or protein. Here's the breakdown:

1 gram of carbohydrate	=	4 calories
1 gram of protein	=	4 calories
1 gram of fat	=	9 calories

Some experts also believe that fat calories are converted into body fat more readily than the same number of carbohydrate or protein calories. What better reason to emphasize fruits, vegetables, salads and grains! The message is clear: reduce the fat in your diet and you're well on your way to being healthier and controlling your weight.

How to reduce your fat intake

1: Cut fat *calories, not just calories*

Here are some ways in which you can cut fat calories from your diet:

Instead of ...
- fried foods
- butter

- red fatty meat

- hard cheese

- chips
- cake
- crisps
- ice-cream
- mayonnaise
- salad dressing
- cream sauce

Try ...
- baked or grilled foods
- low fat spreads or low-sugar jams
- fish, skinless chicken, lean meat
- low-fat cheese, cottage cheese
- baked or boiled potatoes
- plain bread roll
- crispbreads
- low-fat yoghurt, ices
- low-fat dressings
- low-fat dressings
- tomato or wine sauce

- sour cream
- whole milk

- low-fat yoghurt
- skimmed milk

2: Read labels

You don't need to be a nutritionist to read labels wisely. Look for the number of calories and quantity of fat per portion. More and more product labels now carry this information.

It is widely acknowledged by experts that we should limit the fat in our diets to 30 per cent or less of our total daily calories. To apply this to the products we purchase, just remember there should be no more than 3 grams of fat per 100 calories. We know that each gram of fat has 9 calories. So, for every 100 calories of a particular food, only about 27 calories (3 grams at 9 calories each) should be from fat. Remember, too, that your *total* daily food intake needs to include 30 per cent or fewer of its calories from fat.

3: Change to healthier fats and oils

Some fats are definitely better than others. 'Saturated fats' are the enemy. These types of fats raise blood cholesterol levels – a dangerous condition that can lead to heart disease and stroke. Here are some guidelines.

Choose . . .
- monounsaturated fats (olive, peanut and rape-seed oils)
- polyunsaturated fats (saf-flower, corn and soya oils, margarine)

Avoid . . .
- animal fats, dripping, suet, lard
- cream
- 'hydrogenated' vegetable oils (they are more satu-rated)
- tropical oils, such as palm or coconut oil (they're often hydrogenated)

4: Watch out for and avoid hidden fats

Some sources of fat are obvious – butter, whole milk, fatty beef and so on – but there's also a lot of fat hiding in processed and packaged foods. Baked goods, dairy substitutes, biscuits, luncheon meats, pâtés, hot dog and other sausages, egg and tuna salads, to give just a few examples.

5: Learn to listen to your body's hunger and satisfaction messages

Duke University researchers in North America found that many adults who were prone to being overweight and who frequently went on and off diets were unaware of their bodies' messages of hunger and satisfaction. They were people who responded more to the clock and to other external cues than to their bodies' internal hunger signals. Recapture the natural human response to food: eat when you're hungry and stop when you're full. People who do so rarely need to diet!

6: Cultivate the art of substitution

Many people prefer fatty foods because they like the taste. The good news is that high-quality natural foods can be used as delicious alternatives to most high-fat foods – from bacon to butter. Here are some ways you can make yourself a creative expert on these alternatives:

- borrow or buy some low-calorie cookbooks and experiment
- do a course in low-fat gourmet cooking
- see a nutritionist to learn how to substitute healthy, tasty, low-fat ingredients for your favourite high-fat foods.

7: Discover the weight that's right for you

If you're not sure what you should weigh, you may want to discuss this with your doctor.

To lose an average of a pound a week, the 'rule of 10' will

tell you roughly how many calories to consume. Convert your weight into pounds and multiply by ten. For example, if you weigh 160 pounds, your daily calorie allowance will be approximately 1,600 calories.

This 'rule of 10' is a useful guide if you have less than 25 pounds to lose. If you need to lose more than 25 pounds, ask your doctor for an appropriate calorie allowance.

Beware of losing weight too *fast!*

You may be tempted to try to lose weight as fast as you can – especially if there's a special forthcoming event you 'want to be slim for'. The word from the experts, though, is to go slowly and be patient. A slow, gradual weight loss is much more effective in the long run. A regular 0.5 to 1kg (1 to 2lb) weight loss per week is ideal (and it adds up faster than you think!). Losing weight slowly gives you time to solidify new eating habits, and it gives your body time to adjust. Besides, a rapid weight loss usually represents an initial loss of water and muscle rather than fat, so weight loss this way is easily regained. Therefore, go slowly to make sure the weight you lose is gone for good.

8

Exercise –
Make it Part of Every Day!

If you want to stay healthy and make your weight loss permanent, you just can't do without exercise. Along with cutting down on the fat you eat, exercising regularly may be your best ally in improving your all-round health and bringing your weight under lasting control.

How can I come to enjoy exercising, so that I'll keep doing it?

If you don't enjoy, or give up when it comes to exercise, you probably haven't tried hard enough to find a form of exercise you like! Exercise doesn't have to mean running laps around a track or doing five miles on a stationary bike. Don't give up until you find an exercise that truly satisfies you. When you do, you'll know because you'll *want* to do it and you'll miss it when something keeps you from it.

The only exercise I've ever done is walking. How can I find out about other types of exercise I might like?

Walking is excellent exercise at any age, but there are countless other choices. One good way to experiment with different forms of exercise is to join a gym or health club on a trial basis. You'll be able to try out machines that exercise the heart and lungs, the swimming pool, the tennis, badminton or squash courts, and much more. If one activity doesn't suit you, try again until you find one that does! In the beginning, go slowly. If you're overweight and new to exercise, it would be wise to discuss your plans with your doctor first.

Why is exercise so important?

Studies have shown that overweight people don't necessarily eat more than slimmer people, but they do exercise a lot less! Experts don't understand exactly why, but regular exercise seems to 'speed up' the metabolism slightly – even after the actual exercise period is over. If you lower your consumption of calories and fat without increasing your physical activity, you'll be ignoring one of your most powerful weight-loss allies. Regular exercise can help make the difference between permanently losing weight and failing to do so.

Regular exercise:

- means you burn more calories – even after your workout has ended
- helps bring your appetite under control – it may even make you less hungry than before
- gives you an overall sense of confidence and well-being: it puts you back in control of your body
- convinces you that you *can* make positive changes
- tones and firms your body
- improves your overall health – from your lungs and heart to your bones and skin, regular exercise helps keep you healthy and strong
- provides a great 'alternative behaviour' to eating – especially when you're not hungry
- clears your head – it can make you more alert and able to concentrate
- makes you feel good – it can help you feel stronger, physically and emotionally, with a greater zest for living, and exercise causes the brain to release certain chemicals that can actually change your mood, creating a more positive state of mind.

Plan your exercise periods

Schedule your exercise time just as you plan your other activities for the day. Treat this time as an important appointment you don't want to miss. Ask your family or those you work with to help you keep that special time free.

My schedule is so unpredictable. I can't count on having the same time free every day for exercising. What can I do?

Be flexible! Don't be afraid to switch to a different time or a different kind of exercise on days that are especially busy. If you can't get to the pool for your usual swim, don't give up. Be creative! Schedule a walk between meetings. Use your ten-minute break to climb several flights of stairs. (Again, remember, if you're just starting out, you should check with your doctor about what's appropriate for you and increase speed and frequency gradually.)

Stay active!

You don't have to wait for your planned exercise time – every day offers dozens of opportunities to stay active. Here are some practical ways in which you can keep moving. You'll boost your energy level, improve your health and help your diet too!

- Take the stairs instead of the lift or escalator.
- Get off the tube or bus a few stops early or park further away from work and walk.
- At work or at home, volunteer to 'go to get things'.
- Walk instead of drive.
- Jog or run on the spot while you wait for the bus.

We recommend walking

Walking is an ideal way to enjoy healthy, aerobic exercise without putting too much stress on your body. It can perk up

48

your thinking and help you feel relaxed and invigorated. A serious walker can shed quite a bit of excess weight while toning-up muscles.

Many people take regular walks for the sheer fun and exhilaration of it! They develop special routes and report a heightened awareness of everything around them – nature, other people, architecture and so on, all the things you miss in a car. Some walkers even report an enhanced sense of hearing, sight and smell.

Even at a quick pace, walking is relaxing and rhythmic. You may find it especially easy to focus your thinking and concentration as you walk, and a regular walk is an ideal time to begin to reprogramme your thinking with positive, self-strengthening thoughts.

Keep your pace brisk

Casual walking

This includes window-shopping, light strolling or short trips around the house or garden. This leisurely pace can be delightfully refreshing, but don't expect significant health or fitness benefits to result from it!

Aerobic walking

For most people, a pace of about 120 steps per minute – which equals about 4 miles an hour for the average man and 3 miles an hour for the average woman – will get the heart and lungs working. Setting a running machine for between 3 and 5 miles per hour can give you a sense of this aerobic pace. Getting your heartbeat to increase and your breathing to deepen, this is the kind of walking you're after!

9

Be Assertive –
Ask for the Help You Need!

Sticking to a diet is rarely a solo performance – other people can affect the success or failure of your efforts. From family members who insist on giving you all the wrong snacks, to people you work with bringing 'treats' to work, to friends who invite you to dinner – other people certainly can influence your willpower and determination. But you can teach your family, friends and workmates to help, not hurt, your efforts. All you need do is tell them openly and honestly about your diet – and then stick to your plan.

I never know what to say when other people are eating foods I'm avoiding and offer me some. Usually, I just give in. What should I do?

Remain firm. Remind yourself of your goals. If people coax you to join them, tell them about the changes you are making. Ask for their co-operation, then stick to your plans! They can be an important asset in your efforts to stick to your diet.

My family doesn't understand how hard it is for me to follow a diet. They tell me to stick to it, but they don't do anything to help me out.

Don't assume that the people around you know how to be sensitive to what you are trying to do. After all, they can't read your mind. Your family and friends may need to be 'trained'. Tell them, clearly and specifically, *how* to be helpful. The suggestions in the rest of this chapter will get you started.

Be assertive: ask for what you want

Here are five requests to make of your family and friends:

- do not snack in front of me
- do not bring high-fat foods into the house
- respect my efforts to stick to my diet and don't tempt me
- encourage me
- remind me of my goals when I weaken and suggest non-food distractions.

If you feel uncomfortable asking for this kind of help, you may be telling yourself:

- I shouldn't need any help
- It's embarrassing to admit that I need help
- I couldn't stand it if I asked for help and was refused
- I should be strong enough to do this by myself.

These ideas are illogical and self-defeating. Consider instead the following healthy self-statements:

- we *all* need help with some things
- other people often feel good about helping
- it's human nature to want to help
- no one can do everything alone
- there's nothing wrong with asking for help – it's worse *not* to ask
- asking for help and being refused is unfortunate, but it's not a catastrophe and at least you will have asked!

Make requests, not demands

Ask for what you want, but don't *demand* it. This way, you give the other person room to say no. And sometimes they will! However if your request is just that – a request, not a demand – you won't be hurt if you are refused.

Make the best choice

Suppose your family celebrates with big food bashes. You've explained that you're on a diet, but they still act insulted unless you join in and eat a lot. Let's examine your options:

- go to the party, stick to your guns and eat only what you should *despite* family pressure
- decide not to go to the party and not be pressured.

Which should you choose? Neither option is ideal. In a case like this, you simply have to make the best choice you can while keeping in mind your goals. Remember, you have the right to put your self-interests first, even if it means putting friends and family at a close second. It's your life, your body and your health – it's *your* choice!

You can say no!

If you have trouble saying no, you may be too concerned about getting other people's approval. That's self-defeating. People will not always feel the same way you do. For example, suppose you're eating out with friends who pressure you to eat more, taste their choice from the menu, share their desserts and so on. They may be annoyed if you resist, but don't back down! Your job is to do what's best for *you*. Politely but firmly say *no*. Your friends will soon learn you mean it.

Tell people what you like!

When you're pleased with someone's attempt to help your efforts to stick to your diet, say so. People like to be appreciated, and they'll probably be encouraged to continue doing more of the same!

Most people are going to be co-operative and helpful, but not everyone will respect your needs. Some will feel threatened and jealous of you. They may even try to tempt you to indulge yourself. Remind yourself that you, not other people, control your decisions.

Practise being assertive

Here are two exercises that will help get you started.

1: Go ahead, ask!

Think of something you'd like to ask someone to do for you – something you might not normally ask. For example, you might ask the hostess of a party you're attending to serve at least one low-fat dish for you or to permit you to bring one yourself. *Now, actually ask her.*

Repeat this on two more occasions. Notice how much easier asking becomes as you do it more. Remember, if you are turned down, you can always try again with someone else. You have the right to ask, and others have the right to say no.

2: Practise saying no

The next time a restaurant meal is not served according to your specifications, send it back! Restaurants are in the business of serving people and most will tailor your order to your needs. If the food was prepared incorrectly, simply don't accept it. Politely, but firmly, say no. How does it feel? Remember, saying no to the waiter is better than saying yes to unnecessary calories and fat!

10

Stick to Your Diet –
You *Can* Do It This Time!

Finally, I've stuck to my diet and reached my goal. But who's to say I can keep it up?

You say so! Rational control of your eating and weight means finally changing your relationship with food. And you know how to do it! We've talked about many of these changes in this book, including exercising regularly, changing your behaviour, handling stress more constructively, reducing your fat intake, thinking more rationally and eating to satisfy hunger instead of emotional needs.

That's a lot of things to change. I'm just beginning my diet and I'm not sure where to start

Start by setting concrete, realistic goals for yourself, then pursuing each one gradually, one at a time. Go back through the chapters of this book and select a few short-term goals for each week. For example, if you are just beginning your diet, you might decide to keep a daily food log (to teach yourself about your actual eating habits now), start walking briskly for 20 minutes or longer each day and switch to low-fat or non-fat foods wherever possible. Then, as you meet these goals one week, set yourself one or two new ones for the following week.

Some more helpful tips

The following tips will make it easier to stick to your diet and more certain that you will succeed.

1 Eat regularly. Don't skip meals, especially breakfast. This

can make you hungrier and cause you to overeat. Pay attention to your body's hunger signals.

2   Keep fattening foods out of the house.

3   If you find yourself getting into bad habits again or regaining the weight you've lost, go back on your diet right away. Lapses are common when you're changing a lifetime's habits, so don't let a slip throw you. Just stick to your diet strictly until you are eating properly again and your weight's back being ideal again.

4   Have a light, low-fat snack before going out to social engagements that involve eating. (Then eat lightly.)

5   Avoid emotional eating. Learn to relax and to handle stress more appropriately.

6   Drink several glasses of water daily to take the edge off hunger and to fill you comfortably.

7   Avoid or reduce your intake of alcohol, salt, fried foods and sugar.

8   Keep a diary of the food you eat (such as the one on page 34). This is especially useful at the beginning of your diet when you most need to learn about your eating habits.

9   Have crunchy vegetables and fruits for snacks.

10 Serve good, healthy food on attractive dishes. Enjoy the experience.

11 Brush your teeth after you eat, as a signal to yourself that the meal (and eating) is over.

12 Stop eating before you feel overfull.

13 Keep with you a list of alternative activities that can substitute for eating when you're tempted to eat because you're restless, bored or looking for something to do.

14 Carry a 'before' picture with you that reminds you why you started your diet.

15 Find substitutes for fats and oils in foods and in cooking. Use more herbs and spices for flavour.

16 Eat slowly. Savour the taste of your food.

Some tips for when you eat out

1 Water, wine spritzers and soda water are excellent substitutes for alcohol.
2 As starter, select a salad or non-oily vegetable dish.
3 Have bread without butter or margarine.
4 Order a light salad dressing on the side; then you know exactly how much you are having. Avoid salad extras, too, such as cheese, bacon or croutons.
5 Consider ordering a starter as your main dish or sharing your main course with a friend.
6 Order main courses that are grilled or baked. Avoid those that are fried or come with rich sauces.
7 Trim visible fat from meat or, preferably, order lean cuts, such as filet mignon, sirloin, fillet, rump or entrecôte. Avoid high-cholesterol meats, such as liver. Choose chicken without the skin and in preference to duck or goose.
8 Choose tomato-based sauces rather than rich, creamy ones for pasta dishes.
9 Order vegetables steamed or boiled, not fried. Avoid butter-drenched vegetables.
10 Top your baked potato with yoghurt or mustard instead of butter, cheese or sour cream.
11 Select fresh fruit, granitas or sorbets for dessert.

Some tips for parties

1 Select your food *once*. Rule out second helpings.
2 Find out what's on the menu and, if appropriate, consider bringing your own low-fat dish.
3 Have a fruit or vegetable snack before the party so that you don't arrive feeling too hungry.
4 Before the party, use your rational-emotive techniques (see

page 25) to picture yourself successfully handling the temptations you'll encounter.

5 Eat with moderation.

Some tips for travellers

1 Try to find out what kind of food will be available. Spend some time *before* the trip planning appropriate alternatives and variations that suit your needs.

2 Carry food with you as you travel. Low-fat snacks like fruit, plain rolls and tinned tuna (in brine, not oil) are a good food reserve.

What about motivation?

Motivation is the 'fuel' that keeps you moving towards your goal. But don't wait until you feel super-motivated to start your diet. Nothing will motivate you faster than actually taking action and seeing progress! The following simple exercise will boost your motivation even more.

On an index or blank postcard, fill both columns below with as many examples as you can think of. Carry the card with you and add new ideas as you think of them. We've started you off with a few common thoughts; now you continue with your own.

Costs of bad habits	*Benefits of sensible eating*
• Discomfort	• Weight loss
• Clothes don't fit	• Clothes fit and look great
• Poor health	• Better health
• Feel like hiding	• Compliments on my looks
• Feel sloppy, sluggish	• Feel trim, energetic

Keep adding to the list over time and refer to it at least twice daily. This list will help you defeat temptation, renew your goals and stick to your diet.

Congratulations

At this point, you have everything you need to succeed in your efforts to stick to your diet. With a sensible plan and the information about rational eating and weight control you have discovered in this book, you're on your way to a healthy and slimmer new you.

Finally, we wish you the best of luck and health in your endeavours. You will not regret taking control of food, no longer letting *it* control *you*.

11

Case Studies

For change to occur, we need to put theoretical concepts into concrete practice. This chapter illustrates clients at work and clearly demonstrates that Rational Emotive Behaviour Therapy works if *you* work it!

It's not what you eat, it's what's eating you!

Jane came to counselling asking for help with depression and compulsive eating. It became clear that both Jane's depression and out-of-control eating were linked to the recent break-up of a long-term relationship. Her boyfriend had found someone else and walked out. Jane's friends tried to convince her that she'd meet someone else, that she was young and would have many more opportunities. However, their attempts at cheering Jane up were failing and finally Jane sought professional advice.

Our work was first to identify the main belief that was troubling Jane. Her friends had failed because Jane's concerns about future prospects were minimal. Jane was more upset about herself. She blamed herself for the break-up and felt she was an inadequate person. Jane's self-downing created her depression as well as the compulsive eating she engaged in to drown her misery.

Step 1 was to help Jane see that the break-up was not creating her depression and compulsive eating, but rather it was her irrational beliefs that were at the core of her problem.

Step 2 was to teach Jane how to dispute or challenge her illogical thinking. Together we composed the following disputes:

1 How does Bob's rejection of me make me an inadequate person?

2 Even if this break-up were my fault (and that's not clear), how does that make me a worthless individual?

3 Who says that because Bob doesn't want me, no one else will?

4 Why do I need someone in my life to be happy and feel good about myself?

Step 3 was to teach Jane how to answer the above and to generate some new effective rational beliefs to replace her old self-sabotaging irrational ideas. Jane came up with the following replacements:

1 Bob may not want to be with me any more, but that doesn't mean that I'm no good or unlovable. His rejection reflects his wishes, not my adequacy.

2 One person can't assume responsibility for the total relationship. It takes two people to make and break a relationship. Making mistakes means I'm human, not worthless. I can certainly learn some good lessons from this situation. My father always used to say to me, 'Live and learn, if you learn'. I can certainly learn from my mistakes.

3 Because Bob doesn't want me, doesn't mean no one else will.

4 I don't need Bob to feel good about myself and enjoy other things in my life.

5 I may have less attention now, but that doesn't mean I'm less of a person.

6 I don't like getting rejected, but I certainly can endure and survive it.

7 There's no reason why everyone I like has to feel and keep feeling the same way about me. I also change my mind about who I like to be with. People's interests and desires change.

Jane read the above list of new rational beliefs out loud. When she finished I asked her how she felt. She replied that the ideas really made sense and just hearing herself say them helped her feel much better. She could feel the depression lifting. Although she still felt sad (which was appropriate), she no longer felt so immobilized and bad about herself. After reviewing and working with these new ideas at home for one week, Jane reported she was eating less compulsively and more in response to hunger and energy cues rather than to feed her depressed spirit.

Jane was learning an important distinction. Painful things happen in life but we can learn to have healthy negative feelings (sadness) as opposed to unhealthy crippling responses (depressions and compulsive eating). Our reactions to events are largely determined by our beliefs and interpretations of these happenings. Or as Epictetus in the 1st century AD put it, 'Men are disturbed not by things, but by the views which they take of them.'

Finally, I emphasized to Jane that for change to be lasting, it would be vital for her to repeat her new rational beliefs to herself (using a tape, out loud, in writing, etc.) frequently and forcefully in order to reduce her emotional (depression) and behavioural (compulsive eating) responses now and in the future. Some experts believe that it takes at least 30 days to change a habit. Jane spent the next month diligently chipping away at her old self-defeating beliefs replacing them with her new effective rational beliefs.

Self-acceptance

Accepting the unacceptable

Abbey complained in every session about her 'unacceptable body features and parts'. Her 'stomach was too round, and her thighs too chunky, and her legs too wide'. Her dissatisfaction with her body was a constant source of torment. Not only did she obsess constantly, but she limited her participation in otherwise fun activities (dancing, swimming), because of her shame and body-loathing.

She was finally convinced that hating her body wasn't going to change it and that she would be better off putting more energy into modifying her self-defeating 'body-bashing' and less energy into beating herself up.

Abbey gained her best results with the following self-help exercise. Since Abbey was a writer, she was assigned the task of writing an ode to each unacceptable body part. However, her task was to force herself to find something likeable, helpful and positive about these previously unacceptable body parts. Using her creativity, Abbey focused on the function of each body part; how her thighs, legs, stomach, etc. served her and helped her to function with good health and excellent mobility.

This exercise was an eye-opener for Abbey. It helped her to look at a previously 'unacceptable' condition just differently enough to help her stop torturing herself. Abbey still strongly preferred that her body 'look' different, but she now had a new respect and appreciation for her body's functioning and operation.

Since she was no longer continuously miserable, she had more energy available and determined to do what she could with diet and exercise to change and shape her body. But she was determined to keep a sane perspective and memorized the popular 'Serenity Prayer' to guide her efforts:

Lord, grant me the serenity to accept the things I cannot change; the courage to change the things I can; and the wisdom to know the difference.

At what weight am I okay?

Carolyn did not feel okay about herself unless her weight

stayed under 110 pounds. Carolyn defined her self-worth in terms of how many pounds she weighed and which jeans would fit. Finally, Carolyn got tired of yo-yo-ing between loving and hating herself and asked for help.

She slowly began to realize that although there were many advantages to her being thinner – her clothes looked and felt better on her – there was no advantage to condemning herself when her weight climbed. Carolyn determined to work at accepting herself no matter what the scale showed. In fact, she agreed to stop allowing the scale to be the arbiter of her daily moods. Carolyn put the scale away and checked her weight only once weekly instead of every other hour.

She practised tolerating the discomfort of the extra pounds and then actually reassessed an appropriate body weight with her physician. She acknowledged her expectations were somewhat unrealistic and the source of unnecessary self-pressure.

Carolyn bought new clothes, somewhat larger, but in a size she was more easily able to maintain. Maybe next lifetime she'd reinvent herself as Twiggy, but for the rest of this life, Carolyn determined that she was okay the way she was!

Secret meanings of food

'If only I were thinner'

Sheryl was a college student. Until she went to college, her weight had not been a problem. Now it was all she talked and worried about. She was convinced that her extra weight was the source of all her difficulties in life – boyfriends, grades, friends, etc. She blamed her lack of success on her extra 30 pounds. 'If only I were thinner, I would be okay,' was her ongoing lament. Only after much work in sessions, did Sheryl begin to recognize that she was using her weight as an excuse for her poor performances.

Sheryl became aware that she was unhappy with her room-mates, but because she had poor assertive skills, she was eating to tolerate the unhappy situation. With coaching in counselling, she began to 'talk up' instead of 'eat up' and tried to change what was changeable and tolerate what was not. At the end of the term she looked into changing room-mates.

Sheryl had also been 'hiding' behind her weight, afraid to have a boyfriend. What she told everyone was that she was too heavy and that no one would be interested. In truth, she was scared, afraid of what would be 'expected of her' and unpractised at saying 'no'. Being overweight was her way of staying 'safe'.

Again, with some solid coaching, Sheryl learned that she had options. She didn't have to sacrifice herself to accommodate anyone else. She had the right to say yes or no as she pleased.

Understanding the powerful message that her extra weight held for her was Sheryl's first step in getting free. Sheryl had used excess food and and her weight to keep her 'safe' and isolated.

Now Sheryl had another choice to make. And she decided to risk being assertive and putting her own interests first. Losing a room-mate or potential boyfriend was a small price to pay for her new-found confidence and comfort.

Sheryl was losing weight, too. Since she was taking care of her feelings in a healthier way, she didn't need the extra and unnecessary calories to calm her down. And because she felt emotionally freer, she had more energy to put into working out and having fun.

Because Sheryl became willing to slowly take more risks, she gradually felt stronger and more in charge of her life and the people in it. She no longer needed the extra food to speak for her. She was doing that herself!

Thou shalt not take thyself too seriously

In our weekly weight control groups, we encourage group members to add this 11th commandment to their personal philosophy of living.

Tom C., a serious group member who was working hard to lose weight, also worked hard not to make the results he was after sacred and necessary immediately.

He arrived at the group one evening and got on the scale to check his weekly progress. Tom had been exercising and eating sensible low fat meals, and had been careful to avoid any emotional eating in the last two weeks. He was sure the scale would reflect his hard work. However, the scale was unchanged and Tom was disappointed.

Refusing to make himself depressed, he simply expressed his regrets as follows, 'In my mind, I've lost weight, and it's just a matter of time until my body catches up with the plan!'

Good work, Tom!

Persistence pays

Joan M., a regular at our weekly weight groups, completed an eight week series and commented that she would benefit from a review. She enrolled for another series of eight, and then another, and then another yet. Joan completed nine series of the eight session group programme before she succeeded in losing weight and in keeping it off.

We encouraged Joan and others to keep coming back because, although many participants lost weight in each group series, unless they kept practising and reinforcing new ideas and behaviours, many of them would put the pounds back on. Old habits die slowly and new techniques require practice, patience, and persistence.

Joan kept coming back until she got what she needed. She

demonstrated the values of persistence and determination, so vital for change.

Changing your diet patterns

Paul J. was overwhelmed at work. He had just been promoted to a supervisory position, requiring longer hours and more work. He was feeling stressed and noticed he was eating more frequently, particularly when he was not hungry.

Paul recognized this as an old pattern of behaviour from his childhood. Paul used the activity of going to look for something to eat as a distraction, as a break from the pressures of work. And he used the eating as a way of getting comfort and relief from the stress.

What did Paul want? He wanted to give up this self-sabotaging behaviour. To accomplish this, we worked with Paul's self-defeating thoughts and then applied a behavioural intervention.

1 First Paul identified a few irrational beliefs that kept him locked into this pattern.
- 'I must have a break.'
- 'I can't stand the stress in the office.'
- 'I'm too anxious, I need some chocolate.'
2 Then Paul disputed and challenged aloud his illogical statements.
- 'Where's the evidence that I must take a break now?'
- 'Where's the proof that I can't stand the stress here? Have I passed out, am I dying?'
- 'Where's it written that I must not be anxious, and that I have to get some chocolate?'
3 Finally, Paul substituted some new effective rational beliefs for his damaging, and self-defeating ideas.
- It's nice to take a break, but I truly don't *have* to. Each time I

run away from stress, and go for food, I keep showing myself that's the way to handle the strain. If I want to learn new reactions, I'd better sit here and create a non-food break, like calling someone, or doing some easier tasks for a while.

- I can stand this stress, although I certainly don't like it. However, it won't kill me. Perhaps I can take a few minutes and close my eyes, listen to some soft music, or do a quick relaxation exercise and try to calm down.
- Sometimes I may feel anxious. I'm human, and it's not the end of the world. It always passes. I don't have to make it worse by running for chocolate. I can try to figure out what I'm worrying about and try to dispute my irrational worries and generate some new saner beliefs that will reduce my anxiety.

Paul made great headway tolerating the office stress without food by repeating to himself forcefully and frequently his new rational beliefs. We reviewed Paul's goal: He wanted to give up his self-defeating behaviour of going for food to escape stress. Paul found the following directive helpful.

Paul was instructed to keep a small notebook handy. Each day he found himself searching for and devouring food to escape the stress of the day, he was to mark the time and day in his notebook. Each infraction would cost him £5.00.

At the end of the week, Paul was to total his violations and send a cheque for that amount to his least favourite political party. Paul soon discovered that his tolerance for stress was growing and he was determined to find non-food techniques to handle his daily emotional strains. He was a staunch conservative and adamant about 'not giving one penny to those socialists'.

Asking for help ... Must it be so difficult?
Laura J. had a job, a family, and a home to care for. Like many

people, she would rush home from work, pick up groceries, prepare dinner, clean up, pay bills, and collapse. She felt overwhelmed and used snacking as a way to calm herself down.

We discussed in session that 'asking for help' might be a more suitable way to make life more comfortable.

However, Laura, like many clients, felt uncomfortable asking for assistance because she believed that:

1 I hate to admit I need help. It's embarrassing.
2 I should be able to handle everything myself.
3 It would be too painful to ask for help and be turned down.

Since Laura recognized she was working on overload, I finally convinced her to experiment and practise some new ideas and behaviours. If she didn't like the results she could always go back to her old system. She agreed and we went to work.

Laura's task was to work at both 'thinking' against and 'acting' against her self-defeating ideas and behaviours.

First we generated some new rational counter messages to replace her self-defeating thoughts:

1 Most people can use help from time to time. I don't have to put myself down and feel ashamed because I too can use assistance. I'm just like other people. Welcome to the human race!
2 No one can do everything alone. We all need help with some things.
3 It's unpleasant to be turned down, but I certainly can stand it. I have a right to ask for help, and other people have a right to say no. If I ask and get turned down, it's not the end of the world. I can try harder to manage on my own or I can ask someone else for help.

At first, the repetition of these new ideas seemed awkward and not very believable to Laura. I explained that this happens with many people. It takes much practice, practice, practice for them to change an 'intellectual understanding' to a real 'emotional integration'.

To facilitate her practice, Laura made a tape of her new beliefs and played it continuously over and over. She would listen to the tape on her walkman on the tube going to and coming from work, while using the exercise bicycle, while jogging outside, and just about anywhere she could. She further repeated out loud her new rational beliefs to herself in private and wrote and rewrote them on notepaper to further embody her new thinking.

Laura was doing well, but we realized that to really have a meaningful change, it was important for Laura to also 'act against' her old philosophy in the following ways.

1 Laura asked her husband to help with the groceries. He said he would. Laura had forgotten that sometimes other people even feel good about helping.
2 She asked her children to do certain tasks at home. They protested, but Laura refused to upset herself with their resistance. She successfully negotiated a deal with them where she got help and they got some extra rewards.
3 Laura asked a friend to help her at work, but the friend said no. At first Laura was upset, but she quickly reminded herself that sometimes people will say no. Asking for help and being refused is regrettable, but hardly a catastrophe. If she really needed the help at work, she could probably ask someone else.

Laura challenged her philosophy that she couldn't ask for help and had to do it all herself. She found the results definitely worth the effort!

Keeping records

Carol wanted to lose weight. She maintained that she hardly ate, she wasn't losing and couldn't understand what the problem was. I suggested charting as a means to gather objective data about what she did with food.

Like many clients, she resisted the idea. She thought it would be a bother and not worth it. I agreed that it was a bother, but that after one or two weeks, we would have a good idea how she dealt with food. I convinced her that the long-term gain would be more than worth the short-term hassle. We would certainly see how, where, how often, and under what conditions Carol was using food.

Carol also worried that she wouldn't chart well enough or completely enough. I encouraged Carol not to be perfectionistic and simply do the best she could. Of course, the more completely she filled in each day, the more information we would have. But some information was certainly better than no information!

Carol reflected that her goal was to lose weight and to have a better relationship with food, so she agreed to keep a food diary.

After two weeks of charting, Carol was amazed to learn just how frequently she was eating. She did eat three sensible meals, but she also ate when she was angry, bored, frustrated, lonely, etc. In other words, Carol was a classic emotional eater. Thanks to the information from the chart, we had our work cut out for us and could begin to teach Carol non-food ways to deal with her emotions.

Getting started

Frequently clients are ambivalent about losing weight. They think they *should* lose weight and pay more attention to their health, but don't really *want* to be bothered. Pam J. came to a session with this dilemma. Not wanting to waste her time or money, I suggested that we first use a technique called 'hedonic calculus'.

The technique is structured like this:

Reasons to diet		*Reasons not to diet*	
1 Health	(4)	1 Feel too deprived	(10)
2 Clothes fit better	(2)	2 Too much bother	(10)
3 More energy	(1)		——
4 Compliments	(1)		20
5 Feel more fit	(1)		
	——		
	9		

The numbers in parentheses after each item are a weighted value reflecting the importance of each item to Pam from 1–10. The 'reasons to' side reflects positive value. The 'reasons not to' side shows negative value.

In the above assessment, although Pam has only two reasons 'not to diet', they have a stronger total negative meaning to her than the total positive value of the five items on the reasons 'to diet' side.

Pam's honesty here was very important in getting a true measure of her real willingness to work on her diet at this particular time. With the help of this exercise, Pam came to see that her commitment to diet was not really there *right now*, as her work was so demanding.

Perhaps when Pam's life was less pressured, her determination would be stronger. We decided to put the diet work on hold, for now, and to first work on helping Pam reduce her anxiety in the workplace. In a few months we would re-evaluate the meaning of the diet question.

Low frustration tolerance

The source of many diet difficulties is rooted in our attachment to a philosophy of 'low frustration tolerance', which is reflected in statements like, 'it's too hard', 'It shouldn't be this much work', 'I shouldn't have to struggle to get results', 'I can't stand being deprived', etc.

Low frustration tolerance reflects an attitude of being unwilling to tolerate or put up with discomfort. Unfortunately on planet Earth, much of daily living involves effort, hassle, challenges, and inconveniences on a regular basis. So until things change, we work to encourage clients to increase their patience and build their tolerance for the headaches of daily existence.

Rita K. was always on a diet. She came to therapy feeling over-frustrated with the amount of time and energy it took to manage her weight. She was angry and ready to quit her diet programme.

We discussed that Rita certainly could quit the programme. She didn't 'have to' continue to monitor her weight and exercise regime. But, if she quit, she'd better be prepared to accept the possibility that she might gain weight and get out of shape.

For Rita to maintain her weight and figure, diet and exercise were essential. She was not someone who was 'naturally thin'. She had to work at it.

Rita recognized that although weight control for her was hard work, she was making it *even harder* by moaning and groaning about the difficulty and unfairness of her situation.

She realized that her 'demand' to have it easy was irrational. For her, weight control was work, as it is for many people. There was no reason why it *had* to be easier. Although it would be nice to have a different metabolism and body build, she didn't! Rita concluded that although she didn't like her situation, that it would be better for her emotional health if she would try to more gracefully 'lump' it.

Rita had a cousin who was a concert pianist. This cousin practised eight hours daily to maintain peak performance. Recognizing that even 'naturally' talented musicians found it necessary to keep a rigorous commitment to their craft, helped Rita accept that if she wanted to maintain an acceptable level of health and fitness this would require stringent adherence to her diet programme. To maintain her goal required ongoing vigilance to her diet programme, perhaps for life. Only she could decide if the effort was worth it.

Rita had a neighbour who was a writer. This man spent his day at his computer firmly rooted to his seat. Rita interviewed him and asked how he did it. He replied, 'I keep focused on my goal. If I allow myself the luxury of distraction, I'm not effective.'

Rita wanted to be effective and successful at her diet. So she integrated the message . . . 'keep focused on my goal, and increase my frustration tolerance.'

The work for most dieters is long-term and ongoing. Losing weight is only the first step. The main work is the ongoing maintenance!

Favourite group exercises

In running weight control groups, one practice exercise stands out as particularly useful, both in terms of enjoyment and learning value. To help clients challenge their self-defeating beliefs and adapt more self-serving ideas, we developed this exercise:

Directions

1 Look below at the following list of typical self-defeating beliefs (adapted from Albert Ellis' tape, *I'd like to Stop But*)

2 Circle your self-defeating beliefs that sabotage your diet programme.

3 Choose a partner and prepare one person – person A – to talk first and then switch roles with person B.

4 Person A begins by telling Person B which self-defeating idea is sabotaging their diet. Person B then takes on this belief as though it were his or her own.

5 Person A then gets to practise disputing or challenging the logic and wisdom of Person B's holding on to this nutty belief. Person B persistently holds onto the irrational idea until Person A successfully convinces them of the disadvantages and uselessness of the belief.

(Person A is really attacking and challenging his or her own illogical thinking in this role play!).

6 Partners then switch and Person B gives Person A his or her self-defeating belief and proceeds for the next few minutes to attack and challenge the reasons for holding onto this belief.

Each person is given approximately 4–5 minutes to dispute his/her irrational belief and then the group leader has them switch roles. A lively meaningful learning discussion always follows.

Here is a list of some of the most common self-defeating beliefs related to diet that evolve from group discussion. Group members use this list as a guide, and may also add and choose their own unique irrational ideas to the list for the purpose of practice.

Which ones are most familiar to you?
- I can't stand being deprived!

- I've failed so many times at dieting, it proves I can't do it.
- Other people can diet successfully, but not me (I'm no good).
- It's my nature to over-eat. I can't help it.
- I need immediate gratification.
- Life is too boring without sweets. I must have them!
- It will be easier to start dieting tomorrow!
- It's not only hard to diet. It's awful!
- If I diet, I'll feel anxious, and I can't bear feeling anxious.
- I can't resist temptation. I have no willpower.
- It's not fair to have to diet and give up such pleasure.
- Why stop? The damage is already done.
- I need to be motivated to diet and I'm not. Why bother?
- It's awful that I'm like this – my body, age, metabolism!
- You should help me. How can I diet if you eat that food in front of me? You should diet too!

Add your own unique irrational belief, if we've missed it on the above list!

Variation

A variation on this exercise that is also popular in the group is to give each group member a slip of paper on which they are instructed to write down the self-defeating belief which has the strongest hold on them.

We then pass the hat and each member folds their paper and deposits their irrational belief.

One member at a time pulls from the hat an irrational belief (usually someone else's). They present this belief to the group as if it is their own and it then becomes a group effort to talk the person out of this self-defeating idea. Frequently, other members share this belief as well. Thus, many members of the group will benefit from active disputing, thus helping themselves as well as other members.

As humans we learn through repetition and practice. If the practice is fun, and the repetition is varied, the learning and integration may be more lasting and meaningful.

So we end this book by urging you to work hard at changing your irrational beliefs, but vary your practice and have as much fun along the way as possible.

Further Reading

Ellis, Albert, *I'd Like to Stop, But . . .*, (cassette recording), New York: Institute for Rational-Emotive Therapy, 1978.

Ellis, Albert and Harper, Robert A., *A New Guide to Rational Living*, North Hollywood, CA: Wilshire Book Company, 1975.

Lazarus, Arnold, *In the Mind's Eye*, New York: Rawson Associates Publishers Inc, 1979.

Maultsby, Jr., M. C. and Ellis, Albert, *Techniques for Rational-Emotive Imagery*, New York: Institute for Rational-Emotive Therapy, 1974.

Orbach, Susie, *Fat is a Feminist Issue*, London: Hamlyn, 1978.

Smith, Manuel, J., *When I Say No I Feel Guilty*, New York: Bantam Books, 1973.

Young, Howard, S., *A Rational Counseling Primer*, New York: Institute for Rational-Emotive Therapy, 1974.

Keeping a food diary

Each number below relates to a column on the chart on page 35. The filled-in example on page 34 will illustrate what to write in each column.

1: Write down the date

Use a new sheet for each day. You may need two or more sheets per day, especially at first, depending on how much detail you decide to include.

2: Record times and the strength of your hunger

Write down the time of day each time you think about eating – whether you actually eat something or not. Then record how hungry you are by rating the hunger from 1 to 10. A rating of 1 would indicate minimal hunger whereas a rating of 10 would mean you felt ravenous.

In your first week of recording, aim simply to notice your food behaviour. Don't feel guilty about it or even change anything; simply observe. Once you've learnt about your patterns, your goal will be to make an effort to eat *only* when you are hungry but without waiting until you're famished (which makes it more likely that you'll overeat).

3: Record what you ate

Record what you actually ate and, in brackets, you can put what you may have thought about but decided not to eat. Always include amounts. This column gives you information about:

- What you are now consuming or what you are thinking about eating.
- What you are thinking about eating.

31

The reason for writing down what you eat is that it gives you extra time to evaluate your hunger level and decide either to have the food or choose an alternative activity to eating, if indeed, you are not hungry but, rather, bored or frustrated. Be ruthlessly honest about the foods you eat – no one else need see your records.

4: Report on alternatives to eating

If you had the urge to eat, but did something else instead, write it down in the Alternative behaviour column. This gives you clues about what works for you when you want to resist unnecessary overeating.

5: Record your mood

Are you eating emotionally – that is, when you feel stressed, angry, frustrated or tired? Do you eat differently at these times, compared with eating to satisfy hunger?

6: Write down the context

That is, the room, the company and other conditions in which you are eating. This will help you be more conscious of the precise situations in which you eat. (We discussed eating contexts in more detail in Chapter 3.)

7: Note your self-statements

Self-statements are your 'self-talk' – what you say to yourself when you decide to eat or not to eat. Become aware especially of what you're saying to yourself when you are upset. Your self-talk at such times will be crucial to the decisions you make about eating.

A word of encouragement

Many people have found that keeping a food diary gives them a powerful and permanent new sense of control over their 'emotional eating'. It means you can see exactly *what* you eat, *when*, *where* and even *why*. Quite suddenly, what seemed like out-of-control behaviour begins to seem manageable. So, don't put off writing your daily food record, start it today! (See Table 1.)

TABLE I

1 Date	2 Time/strength of hunger (1–10)	3 Food/liquid consumed	4 Alternative behaviour	5 Mood	6 Context	7 Self-statement
14/5	8.00 a.m. (5)	Coffee 2 poached eggs 1 piece of toast 1 pat butter 1 orange		Rested	Kitchen	It's time to eat breakfast. I'm hungry.
	9.45 a.m. (2)	Biscuit		Angry	Desk	I'm so mad; my boss is so unfair to complain about me in front of others.
	12.15 p.m. (4)	½ grapefruit ½ pot cottage cheese ½ roll, Tea		Discouraged	Cafeteria	I can get back on track. It's lunchtime and I'm hungry.
	3.15 p.m. (1)	(Thinking about getting a chocolate bar.)	Called a good friend.	Edgy/tense	Desk	I'm tense – maybe calling Carol will relax me.